To Mrs. May with
thanks for your
leadership, compassion,
humor and grace. Enjoy
your retirement. You
will be greatly missed!

The Hall Family

THE READING WOMAN

A JOURNAL

CONCEIVED AND EDITED BY MAXINE ROSE SCHUR

POMEGRANATE ARTBOOKS ❖ SAN FRANCISCO

Paula Fox quotes excerpted from "Some Thoughts on Imagination in Children's Literature." In B. Hearne and M. Kaye (eds.), *Celebrating Children's Books*. New York: William Morrow and Company, 1981. Copyright holder: Zena Sutherland Lectureship Fund. Reprinted by permission of William Morrow and Company.

Eudora Welty quotes excerpted from "Eudora Welty: I Worry Over My Stories," by D. L. Keith, *The Times Picayune* (New Orleans), Sept. 1973, secs. 3, 8. Reprinted by permission.

Our thanks to Pushcart Press for permission to reprint from *The Writer's Quotation Book* and *The Reader's Quotation Book*.

Published by Pomegranate Artbooks, Box 6099, Rohnert Park, CA 94927

© 1991 Pomegranate Artbooks

Designed by Bonnie Smetts Design

FIRST EDITION

Printed in Hong Kong

06 05 04 03 02 01 00 99 98 97   16 15 14 13 12 11 10 9 8

The Reading Woman is a celebration of all women who love to read. Whether it's at the close of day or just at the close of a door. Whether it's reading aloud to friends around the fire or suspended, mind and body, in a hammock. Poems or potboilers, fact or fancy, it's the pleasure women find in reading that is presented here.

"*La liseuse,*" the woman reader, was an especially popular subject for mid-nineteenth- and early twentieth-century artists. The old image of woman engaged in such domestic arts as needlework gave way to a new heroine in direct conflict with traditional conventions. This new woman rode bicycles, played tennis, frequented cafes and, most important, sought education. *La liseuse* was the thinking woman (though no less decorative) absorbed in words on a page.

By the 1880s, the height of both the Impressionist movement in France and the Victorian era in England, the little girl or woman set amidst a beautiful landscape and lost in a book became the visual antidote to an increasingly industrialized and urbanized Europe. And sometimes, as in Manet's *Gare Saint-Lazare,* the two worlds, one of inner peace and the other of external power, were juxtaposed.

Indeed, the self-contained world of the reader has been portrayed in an imaginative variety of noisy settings: the absorbed reader in the train car, in the music studio and at the swimming pool. The external world is shut out as another world is brought in. Surroundings evaporate when, in Elizabeth Barrett Browning's words, the reader "plunges soul-forward, headlong, into a book's profound."

The women of the last century lived in a world whose economy, government and culture were dominated by men. Reading books was often their only foray into that world. Yet, ironically, as much as books lead away from ourselves, they lead to ourselves. Knowledge of others brings an understanding of self. "Oh but I identified!" Eudora Welty wrote of her first reading experiences. And perhaps it is this identification, a kind of relationship that flows from reader to writer and back again, that hooks us on books. For ultimately we read not merely to know but to experience and feel. We fall in love with reading because it allows our hearts to beat not only a little more quickly but also in rhythm with the hearts of others.

The enjoyment and value of the reader's transcendent and empathizing experience is expressed here in the words of many important literary women. How relevant their thoughts are to us today, who, in our busy, fast-paced lives, struggle to carve from the day a niche of private time—a time to read.

—Maxine Rose Schur

Certain books come to meet one, as do people. —ELIZABETH BOWEN

Yamashita Shintaro (Japanese, 1881–1966). *Woman Reading*, 1907. Oil on canvas, 39-3/8 x 28-3/4 in.
Bridgestone Museum of Art, Ishibashi Foundation, Tokyo.

_Books are meat and
medicine
and flame and flight and
flower
steel, stitch, cloud and clout,
and drumbeats on the air_

—GWENDOLYN BROOKS

The novel is a game or joke shared between author and reader.

—ANNIE DILLARD

Pierre Auguste Renoir (French, 1841–1919). *Madame Claude Monet Reading*, c. 1872. Oil on canvas, 24-1/16 x 19-13/16 in. Sterling and Francine Clark Art Institute, Williamstown, Massachusetts.

As readers, we proceed by the author's arbitrary direction to his one-time destination: a journey rather strange, hardly in a straight line, altogether personal.

—EUDORA WELTY

Literature is the province of imagination, and stories, in whatever guise, are meditations on life. —PAULA FOX

Winslow Homer (American, 1836–1910). *Sunlight and Shadow*, 1872. Oil on canvas, 40-3/16 x 57-19/32 in.
Courtesy of the Cooper-Hewitt Museum, Smithsonian Institution/Art Resource, New York.
Gift of Charles Savage Homer, 1917–14–7.

In bad weather, when I couldn't go outside, I used to sit on those stairs and extract a "Geographic" as carefully as if I were playing pick-up sticks, so I wouldn't bring the whole attic down on myself. Among the glossy pages of the magazines, I met up with pygmies and Balinese dancers, cities built on water, mountain peaks yet unscaled, desert people and people who lived amid eternal snow, dragonflies and anacondas. On those attic stairs in an old house that seemed always on the verge of collapse, I began to sense huge possibilities. —PAULA FOX

The writer shakes up the familiar scene, and as if by magic, we see a new meaning in it. —ANAÏS NIN

As you read a book word by word and page by page, you participate in its creation, just as a cellist playing a Bach suite participates, note by note, in the creation, the coming-to-be, the existence, of the music. And, as you read and re-read, the book of course participates in the creation of you, your thoughts and feelings, the size and temper of your soul.

—URSULA K. LE GUIN

Only one hour in the normal day is more pleasurable than the hour spent in bed with a book before going to sleep, and that is the hour spent in bed with a book after being called in the morning. —ROSE MACAULAY

James McNeill Whistler (American, 1834–1903). *Pink Note: The Novelette*, c. early 1880s. Watercolor on paper, 9-15/16 x 6-1/8 in. Courtesy of the Freer Gallery of Art, Smithsonian Institution, Washington, D.C. 02.158.

Repeat reading for me shares a few things with hot water bottles and thumb-sucking: comfort, familiarity, the recurrence of the expected.

—MARGARET ATWOOD

Frederick Carl Frieseke (American, 1874–1939). *Woman Seated in a Garden*, 1914. Oil on canvas, 26 x 32 in.
The Huntington Library, Art Collections and Botanical Gardens, San Marino, California.

My main disappointment was always that a book had to end. And then what? But I don't think I was ever disappointed by the books. I must have been what any author would consider an ideal reader. I felt every pain and pleasure suffered or enjoyed by all the characters. Oh but I identified! —EUDORA WELTY

We read books to find out who we are. What other people, real or imaginary, do and think and feel . . . is an essential guide to our understanding of what we ourselves are and may become.

—URSULA K. LE GUIN

James McNeill Whistler (American, 1834–1903). *Harmony in Green and Rose: The Music Room*, 1860–61. Oil on canvas, 37-5/8 x 27-7/8 in. Courtesy of the Freer Gallery of Art, Smithsonian Institution, Washington, D.C. 17.234.

_____

_____

_____

_____

_____

_____

_____

_____

_____

_____

_____

_____

Your family sees you as a lazy lump lying on the couch, propping a book up on your stomach, never realizing that you are really in the midst of an African safari that has just been charged by elephants, or in the drawing room of a large English country house interrogating the butler about the body discovered on the Aubusson carpet.

Reading is an escape, an education, a delving into the brain of another human being on such an intimate level that every nuance of thought, every snapping of synapse, every slippery desire of the author is laid open before you like, well, a book. —CYNTHIA HEIMEL

Her eye, her ear, were tuning forks, burning glasses, which caught the
minutest refraction or echo of a thought or feeling. . . . She heard a deeper
vibration, a kind of composite echo, of all that the writer said,
and did not say. —WILLA CATHER

Henri Fantin Latour (French, 1836–1904). *La Liseuse (The Reader)*, 1861. 3 ft. 3-1/4 in. x 2 ft. 8-3/4 in.
Musée d'Orsay, Paris. © Photo R.M.N.

Oh! For a book, and a cosy nook
And oh! For a quiet hour,
When care and strife and worry of life,
Have lost their dreaded power,
When you read with zest the very best
That mind to mind can give,
And quaff your joy without alloy,
And feel it is good to live.

—ANONYMOUS

Edward Hopper (American, 1882–1967). *Interior (Model Reading)*, 1925. Watercolor over pencil on ivory
woven paper, 35.3 x 50.6 cm. © 1991 The Art Institute of Chicago. All rights reserved.
Gift of Mr. and Mrs. Lewis L. Coburn in memory of Olivia Shaler Swan. 1933.487.

I walke manie times . . . into the pleasant fieldes of the Holye Scriptures, where I pluck up the goodlie greene herbes of sentences, eate them by reading, chewe them up by musing, and laie them up at length in the seate of memorie . . . so I may the lesse perceive the bitterness of this miserable life. —QUEEN ELIZABETH I

There is no frigate like a book

To take us lands away . . .   —EMILY DICKINSON

William McGregor Paxton (American, 1869–1941). *The House Maid*, 1910. Oil on canvas,
30-1/4 x 25-1/8 in. In the collection of The Corcoran Gallery of Art, Washington, D.C. Museum purchase.

God forbid that any book should be banned. The practice is as indefensible as infanticide.

—REBECCA WEST

Ruby Aranguiz (American). *Macarina Reading*, 1979. Pastel on paper, 33 x 28 in. Private collection.

*The pleasure of all reading
is doubled when one lives
with another who shares the
same books.*

—KATHERINE MANSFIELD

No entertainment is so cheap as reading, nor any pleasure so lasting.
She will not want new fashions, nor expensive diversions, or variety of
company, if she can be amused with an author.

—LADY MARY WORTLEY MONTAGU

Mary Stevenson Cassatt (American, 1844-1926). *Young Woman Reading*, 1876. Oil on canvas,
13-3/4 x 10-1/2 in. Museum of Fine Arts, Boston. Bequest of John T. Spaulding. 48.523.

If I read a book that impresses me, I have to take myself firmly in hand, before I mix with other people; otherwise they would think my mind rather queer.

—ANNE FRANK

Books are funny little portable pieces of thought.

—SUSAN SONTAG

Edouard Manet (French, 1832–83). *Gare Saint-Lazare*, 1873. Oil on canvas, 36-3/4 x 45-1/8 in.
National Gallery of Art, Washington, D.C.
Gift of Horace Havemeyer in memory of his mother, Louisine W. Havemeyer.

Remorse for the brevity of a book is a rare emotion.

—EMILY DICKINSON

Books are the carriers of civilization. Without books, history is silent, literature dumb, science crippled, thought and speculation at a standstill. They are engines of change, windows on the world, (as a poet said) lighthouses erected in the sea of time. They are companions, teachers, magicians, bankers of the treasures of the mind. Books are humanity in print.

—BARBARA W. TUCHMAN

Albert Joseph Moore (English, 1841–93). *A Reader*, 1877. Oil on canvas, 34-5/16 x 12-9/16 in.
Manchester City Art Galleries, Manchester, England.

And I must read a little Ibsen to compare with Euripides—Racine with Sophocles—perhaps Marlowe with Aeschylus. Sounds very learned; but really might amuse me . . .

—VIRGINIA WOOLF

Theodore Robinson (American, 1852–96). *Two in a Boat*, 1891. Oil on cardboard, 9-1/4 x 13-5/8 in.
©The Phillips Collection, Washington, D.C.

As far as possible I only read what I am hungry for at that moment when I have an appetite for it, and then I do not read, I eat.

—SIMONE WEIL

The greatest gift is the passion for reading. It is cheap, it consoles, it distracts, it excites. —ELIZABETH HARDWICK

John George Brown (American, 1831–1913). *Girl by the Seacoast*, n.d. Oil on canvas, 23 x 17-1/8 in. Courtesy Museum of Fine Arts, Boston. Gift in part of Walstein C. Findlay, Jr., in memory of William Wadsworth Findlay. 61.1294.

Every book is like a purge; at the end of it one is empty . . . like a dry shell on the beach waiting for the tide to come in again.

—DAPHNE DU MAURIER

Once in a very rare year, there comes along a new book, and I say, as I am reading, as my eyes eat words without a blink, as my heart and mind grab each other, This, I say, is The Best Book. I know before the first page is gone. I sense it building. And as the book finishes, I go as slow as I can. I don't want to leave the book's world.

—JILL ROBINSON

Winslow Homer (American, 1836–1910). *The New Novel*, 1877. Watercolor, 9-1/2 x 20-1/2 in.
Museum of Fine Arts, Springfield, Massachusetts. The Horace P. Wright Collection.

_My_ admiration of literature, especially of poetical literature, can never be subdued nor can it be extinguished but with life.

— ELIZABETH BARRETT BROWNING

There are books one needs maturity to enjoy just as there are books an adult can come on too late to savor. —PHYLLIS MCGINLEY

Jacques-Louis David (French, 1748–1825). *Portrait of Madame Buron*, 1769. Oil on canvas, 66.3 x 55.5 cm.
©1991 The Art Institute of Chicago. All rights reserved. Restricted gift of Mrs. Albert J. Beveridge in
memory of her mother, Abby Louise Spencer Eddy 1963.205.

Fiction reveals truths that reality obscures.

—JESSAMYN WEST

Edmund Tarbell (American, 1862–1938). *Girl Reading*. Oil on canvas, 32-1/2 x 28-1/4 in.
Courtesy Museum of Fine Arts, Boston. Charles Henry Hayden Fund. 09.209.

The novel is rescued life.

— HORTENSE CALISHER

Just the knowledge that a good book is awaiting one at the end of a long day makes that day happier. —KATHLEEN NORRIS

Reginald Marsh (American, 1898–1954). *The El*, c. 1928. Oil on canvas, 30 x 40 in.
Collection of Whitney Museum of American Art, New York. Felicia Meyer Marsh Bequest. 80.31.9.

_____

_____

_____

_____

_____

_____

_____

_____

_____

_____

_____

We get no good

By being ungenerous, even to a book,

And calculating profits, so much help

By so much reading. It is rather when

We gloriously forget ourselves, and plunge

Soul-forward, headlong, into a book's profound,

Impassioned for its beauty, and salt of truth—

Tis then we get the right good from a book.

—ELIZABETH BARRETT BROWNING

When I was a ten-year-old bookworm and used to kiss the dust jacket pictures of authors as if they were icons, it used to amaze me that these remote people could provoke me to love. —ERICA JONG

Berthe Morisot (French, 1841–95). *La Lecture (Reading)*, 1888. Oil on canvas, 29-1/4 x 36-1/2 in.
Museum of Fine Arts, St. Petersburg, Florida.

I was reading
Shakespeare's sonnets
when I was thirteen years
old, and I'm perfectly
certain that they made the
most profound impression
upon me of anything I ever
read. That was the turning
point of my life, when I read
the Shakespeare sonnets.

—KATHERINE ANNE PORTER

Marie Spartali Stillman (English, 1844–1927). *Love Sonnets*, 1894. Watercolor on paper, 17-3/8 x 11 in. Delaware Art Museum, Wilmington. Samuel and Mary R. Bancroft Collection, 1935.

Good books, like good friends, are few and chosen; the more select, the more enjoyable.

—LOUISA MAY ALCOTT

I never hesitated, if I happened to finish a particularly wonderful book, to turn around and read it again, right there. I devoured them so quickly, one after another, I'm sure the librarian eyed me as quite peculiar. And you know, I think part of my love for books had to do with what they looked like. I simply adored the printed page, just loved it.

—EUDORA WELTY

Do give books—religious or otherwise—for Christmas. They're never fattening, seldom sinful and permanently personal.

—LENORE HERSHEY

The active scenes are over at my age. I indulge, with all the art I can, my taste for reading. If I would confine it to valuable books, they are almost as rare as valuable men. I must be content with what I can find. The methods may appear low to busy people; but, I forget my infirmities, and attain very desirable ends. —LADY MARY WORTLEY MONTAGU

Rembrandt van Rijn (Dutch, 1606–69). *The Prophetess Hannah (Rembrandt's Mother)*, 1631. Oil on panel, 23-1/2 x 19 in. Rijksmuseum Amsterdam.

Truly each new book is as a ship that bears us away from the fixity of our limitations into the movement and splendor of life's infinite ocean.

—HELEN KELLER

Jean-Honore Fragonard (French, 1732–1806). *The Good Mother*, 1762–63. Oil on canvas, 18-1/2 x 22-1/4 in. The Fine Arts Museums of San Francisco. Gift of Mrs. Herbert Fleishhacker 54.2.

Having created a habit of night reading, my life is a search for longer and longer books. I do not want them to end. . . . But the modern novel, which tends to be subtle rather than profound, entertaining rather than instructive, unmoral and reflective of our chaos, is too disturbing a companion for the long, despondent hours of night. I read them by daylight.

—OLIVIA MANNING

I am always reading or thinking about reading.

—JOYCE CAROL OATES

Sir John Lavery (Irish, 1856–1941). *Girl in a Red Dress by a Swimming Pool.*
The Bridgeman Art Library, London.